IMPERFECT II

IMPERFECT II
poems about perspective:
an anthology for middle schoolers

Edited by
Tabatha Yeatts

History House Publishers

With deep appreciation to Christine Clardy, Dave Dunlap, Sydney Dunlap, Michelle Kogan, Matthew Thompson, Catherine Wingfield-Yeatts, Harry W. Yeatts Jr., Ariana Yeatts-Lonske, Dash Yeatts-Lonske, and Elena Yeatts-Lonske for helping shepherd this project along its way. Tremendous thanks to Benjamin Lonske for bringing it across the finish line.

Cover design and perspectograph artwork by Vivien R. Zhu © 2022

Hardback ISBN-13: 978-0-9679158-5-2
Paperback ISBN-13: 978-0-9679158-6-9
E-book ISBN-13: 978-0-9679158-8-3

Library of Congress Control Number: 2022905002

History House Publishers
Rockville, MD USA

https://ImperfectII.blogspot.com
perspectiveanthology@gmail.com

this book
is dedicated
to artists,
readers,
writers,
and
thinkers

THE PERSPECTOGRAPH

Artist-inventor Leonardo da Vinci was very interested in perspective. He lived from 1452-1512, and at that time it wasn't a given that artists would be able to show a scene with lifelike perspective. They were still figuring out how to do it.

In 1435, Leon Battista Alberti wrote a book called **On Painting**, where he described a method for making paintings on canvas look three-dimensional. Da Vinci learned about Alberti's method and gave it some thought. He wanted his artwork to look three-dimensional, portraying what viewers would see if they looked out a window.

Da Vinci was a resourceful person, not to mention dedicated, so he invented a "perspectograph" – a way to help artists get the most lifelike perspective.

You'll find an image of Leonardo's perspectograph throughout **IMPERFECT II** because, like Leonardo, we are dedicated to pursuing realistic perspectives, too.

Table Of Contents

INTRODUCTION

When artists sit down with a piece of paper or canvas and want to create a realistic scene, they face the challenge of taking something flat (two-dimensional) and using it to portray something with depth (three-dimensional).

In that situation, you want objects in your drawing to reflect the sizes they are – for your mice to look smaller than your houses, for your stars to appear farther away than your roads. With practice, you can keep your picture from looking flat by showing a realistic perspective.

All of us have to do something similar in our daily lives. Things may happen that we view out of proportion – we see them as being bigger, smaller, more permanent than they really are. We need to add perspective to the picture we form every day of our lives and the world.

Have you heard the parable of the blind men and the elephant? It's an old story about four men who have never seen an elephant and try to describe it to each other based on the part they are touching. They each interpret what they're feeling completely differently.

The person who is touching the ear thinks it feels like a fan, whereas the one who touches the tusk thinks it's a spear. The person who feels the tail says it's a rope, and the fourth person touches the leg and guesses it's a tree trunk. In the story, they each think their perspective is the whole picture and believe the others are lying.

People have a lot of thoughts and feelings in common, but their experiences may be different. Someone who has lived through a house fire and someone who has positive memories of camping and cooking over a fire pit might have completely different feelings about the smell of smoke. Both perspectives are reasonable and valid.

Feelings don't have to be the same to make sense. The person who thinks about happy things when they smell smoke might be confused if the person with negative memories runs off. They might even wonder whether they've done something wrong.

It's really easy to assume that our actions cause everything that happens around us. There are plenty of times when that's not true, though. Every day gives us opportunities to learn about other people's perspectives (and to figure out things about our own!).

When we are trying to have a healthy perspective, there are steps we can take. We can strive not to magnify our mistakes in our minds and instead savor our accomplishments, even the tiny ones. We can avoid assuming that everything that happens around us is about us, and we can do our best not to blame ourselves for things we can't control.

In this anthology, you will find poems about all kinds of different perspectives. Sometimes we wish other people understood our point-of-view better, as in **What You Don't See** by Linda Mitchell. Other times we realize we don't even understand ourselves, like François Villon's **All Things Except Myself I Know**.

You will find poems about taking baby steps when we're overwhelmed, such as **Stacking Grampa's Firewood** by Christy Mihaly, and poems about realizing when our thoughts have gone wrong, like **Jumping to Conclusions** by Lisa Varchol Perron. Sometimes what we need is to be compassionate with ourselves and cheer ourselves up – there are poems for that, too.

Poet Lord Byron wrote, "Words are things, and a small drop of ink falling like dew upon a thought produces that which makes thousands, perhaps millions, think."

Let's think about thinking. We're worth the effort!

TABATHA YEATTS

We are all about to go on a journey.
We are the ones we have been waiting for.

THOMAS BANYACYA, SR.

COMPARED TO WHAT?

A pebble isn't all that big
    compared to stones or boulders,
but it's a mountain to the ant
    who lifts it on its shoulders.

And if you were a molecule,
    an atom or a proton,
a water drop would be a lake
    for you to sail your boat on.

An elephant is huge for sure;
    its trunk would crush your scale.
And yet it doesn't seem that large
    if you're a humpback whale.

I've always claimed the Earth is huge,
    and no one has denied it.
And yet the Sun alone could hold
    a million Earths inside it.

Then certainly the *Sun* is huge?
    Well, no, wait just a minute!
The star Mu Cephei could contain
    a billion Suns within it!

Can we agree Mu Cephei's huge?
    The biggest of Red Giants,
it's dwarfed in size by galaxies!
    Believe me! This is science!

The galaxy that it calls home,
    our own, the Milky Way,

contains a hundred billion stars.
    Mu Cephei's *one*, okay?

And though Mu Cephei dwarfs the Sun,
    is bigger and more shiny,
compare it to the Milky Way
    and you will think it's tiny.

And so it goes. The Milky Way,
    astronomers inform us,
although at first it may appear
    mind-bogglingly enormous,

is hardly bigger than a speck,
    when all is said and done.
Of billions and billions of galaxies,
    the Milky Way's just one.

So when you're asked if something's big,
    say, 'I will answer, but...
before I do, please tell me this...
    Big? Compared to *what*?'

ROBERT SCHECHTER

MILA'S HOOP DREAMS

Before the shot, she found her spot,
and gave the ball a kiss.
"This time," she said, "it's going in..."
Then Mila watched it miss.

"One day," she vowed, "I'll do me proud.
I'll sink it through the hole."
So, Mila practiced endlessly
with hopes to make a goal.

And then one night, beneath the light,
inside the city gym,
she shot that ball with skill and grace,
then watched it...
                    hit the rim.

Her father sighed, "At least you tried,
I hope you're not upset."
"I'm great!" she smiled. "A week ago,
I couldn't hit the net!"

WILLIAM PEERY

THOUGHT MACHINE

Sometimes my thought machine makes thoughts like

THAT WENT WELL or YOU'RE DOING GREAT or
YOU'VE GOT THIS

but sometimes it makes thoughts like

THAT WAS TERRIBLE or HOW EMBARRASSING or
WHAT A MESS

When that happens, I dance. Write. Run. Sing.
Listen to music. Talk. Swim.
I think of ONE thing I like about myself

NICE EARLOBES or GREAT DANCING or
EXCELLENT JOKES

and I set about my day.
And somehow, that pesky little thought machine
tends to think more positive things, like

THIS IS GOING WELL, YOU'RE DOING GREAT –
YOU'VE GOT THIS!

And I have.

LAURA MUCHA

You have to learn to see things
in the right proportions.
Learn to see great things great
and small things small.

CORRIE TEN BOOM

MICROSCOPIC THINKING

Help! There's a microscope lodged in my brain
and it magnifies every mistake.
I study my blunders, each minuscule grain
of the faulty decisions I make.

Examined up close, all my failures look LARGE.
Does everyone else see them, too?
Enough! I'm exhausted! It's time I take charge
and challenge this negative view.

Although there's a microscope stuck in my head,
I'll stop it from causing me stress.
My failures exist, but I'll focus instead
on looking at every success!

LISA VARCHOL PERRON

MOUNTAIN MAKER

Don't make a mountain out of a molehill, Mom says
as I diddle daddle dawdle
grumble gripe groan
avoid avoid avoid
my mountain of homework.

I imagine myself a mole
digging an endless burrow through the dark—
tunneling, tunneling,
scooping and piling
pawfuls of soil
into a hill that grows
and grows
and grows.

To a mole, a molehill is monumental.

I hunch over my desk
and claw my pencil,
digging a twisty tunnel
one problem at a time.
Stars slip through the sky
and clouds swallow the moon
while I conquer my mountain of homework,
turning it into a molehill.

BUFFY SILVERMAN

THE BIGGER PICTURE

i am one particle among

millions and

billions and

trillions of us

each of us our own particular

grains and

shapes and

three-dimensional

crystals and

infinitely numerous

colors and

formed through unimaginable

eons and

from uncountable

eruptions and

erosions and

somehow we are all called

sand

HEIDI MORDHORST

POINT OF VIEW

I can see the train on the tracks two blocks away,
but an eagle can see a rabbit two miles away.

I can turn my head to look west down the street to the sunset,
but an owl can turn its head to see 270° in the dark.

I can roll my eyes at Dad's knock-knock jokes,
but chameleons can roll each eye independently.

My eyes are not the best in the animal kingdom,

but I can see both sides of an argument,
giving me the power of perspective,

I can see into your pain,
giving me the power of empathy,

and I can see what might be,
giving me the power of imagination.

MARY LEE HAHN

TRASH OR TREASURE?

We can look at things
in different ways:
A weekend of chaos
or a fun couple days?

A small, measly twig
or a fire starter?
A worthless old watch
or something to barter?

One person's trash
is another's treasure.
What you discard
could be my pleasure.

Choices are choices,
and whatever you say,
I'd choose laughter
any day.

MIA PERRON, *student*

"Eat a live frog first thing in the morning
and nothing worse will happen to you the rest of the day."
~Author unknown, commonly attributed to Mark Twain

FIRST THING

You think I have to eat a frog
the first thing every day.
A frog and I discussed it, though,
and have some things to say.

The frog prefers to live its life.
I'd rather make my bed,
or maybe pull 100 weeds,
or do my math instead.

I'll fold our laundry, clean the toilet—
potty train the dog!
I'd rather do, well, any chore
than swallow a live frog.

The frog and I will thank you, Mom.
Don't listen to Mark Twain.
He may have written classic books
but clearly wasn't sane!

MYRNA FOSTER

MY FACE, SPACE, AND PICTURE DAY

I tell myself
it's just a dot—
     just a spot—
one small red storm on my face…

and my face
     is just a smiling dot—
floating in a sea of school pictures…

and my school
     is just an old brick spot
sprawling on our great, round earth…

and our earth
     is just a green and blue dot
circling our blazing sun…

and our sun
     is just a fiery spot—
shining in the swirling Milky Way…

and the Milky Way
     is a gazillion dots
          with so much dazzle

that I have more to focus on
     than just a dot—
          just a spot—
on the human map of me.

LAURA PURDIE SALAS

Wisdom is not
what you know
but how quickly you adjust
when the opposite proves true.

ROBERT BRAULT

LOCKED OUT

I'm staring at my locker.
I don't know what to do.
My combo isn't working.
I know it ends in 2!

I hear my friends all laughing.
They must have played a trick.
They probably switched my padlock.
I bet they think they're slick.

Some kid comes up to help me.
He opens it just fine.
I ask him how he did that.
He says, "This locker's mine."

TRICIA TORRIBLE

JUMPING TO CONCLUSIONS

Fiona is a friend of mine, the best a friend could be.
I ask her if she'll meet me after school today at three.

She says, "Of course," and so at three, I hurry to our spot.
Some other students come and go. Fiona? She does not!

I wait a little longer, and I start to get a hunch–
Fiona might be mad about a joke I told at lunch.

Fiona has a puppy, a French bulldog she named Stout.
I never should have said, "Does Stout go *oui oui* when you're
    out?"

Perhaps the joke upset her and I sounded like a fool?
And now she'll *never* want to get together after school.

I'm sure she'll just ignore me if I try to start explaining.
But I deserve it! It's my fault. I shouldn't be complaining.

She must be telling everyone I'm stupid, mean, and bad.
I can't believe I lost the closest friend I've ever had!

But wait, who's that approaching? Though my brain is filled
    with fog,
I'm fairly sure it's her–"Fiona!"–and her little dog.

"I'm sorry to be late," she says. "I had to get the pup.
We don't want *oui oui* in the house. You really crack me up!"

LISA VARCHOL PERRON

I'M SORRY

I ripped your pillow.
Your favorite pillow.
Filled with feathers.
Was it your father's?

You ran out crying.
So I am trying
to find each feather
and put it back.

The wind is blowing,
the feathers going
out the window
all over the yard

This fixing pillows
is very hard.

APRIL HALPRIN WAYLAND

21

PIGEON PERSPECTIVES

The bustling city square is filled with cooing
as squads of pigeons squabble in the weeds.
An old man, gently clucking, squats there, strewing
peanuts, breadcrumbs, and some tasty seeds.

A mother pulls her daughter by the hand.
"Those birds are filthy, stay away from there!"
The old man says, "You just don't understand—
so let me introduce this pigeon pair.

"Peg and Sam, here, once were racing birds.
Their ancestors were homing pigeons too.
They carried messages—*Top Secret* words—
through battles, with heroic derring-do."

The man goes on, "They're smart, and squeaky-clean."
"Well, I'm impressed!" says Mom. "We'll watch awhile."
The strutting birds show off and make a scene,
bowing to their partners, square-dance style.

Beguiled, the girl says, "Mama, that one's pretty!
See his neck? It's sparkly purple-green!"
They'd seen pigeons all around the city,
but never paused, till now, to see their sheen.

CHRISTY MIHALY

DERAILLEUR OF THE HEART

Because our conversation
feels like riding a bike uphill,

I think of gears. I think
of how easy it is to shift

lower, how a simple flick
of the thumb makes the impossible

possible. Where are the gears
for love? There must be better

ways to use our teeth
than biting words. There must

be a series of notched wheels
in the heart that allow us

to move forward with less force,
some mechanism to make

the chain hop from one sprocket
to another, changing the way

we engage. I want to find that gadget,
those gears, the ones that help us

hear each other, the ones
that help us say what must be said,

the simple tools that allow us
to move forward at all.

ROSEMERRY WAHTOLA TROMMER

PLANET PIMPLE

I woke up with a pimple.
It's the size of planet Mars,
with a bunch of smaller pimples
scattered near it like the stars.

It's a bulbous, bright red planet,
so immense it nearly glows,
and there's no way to conceal it,
since it's right there on my nose!

When I meet my friend at school,
she just sighs and starts to stare.
I say, "Yep, it's really awful!"
Then she frowns and hides her hair.

She says, "Oh. So you agree, then?"
I'm confused. I answer, "What?"
She says, "Look! My haircut's horrid!"
I say, "Wait...you had it cut?"

DIANA MURRAY

The reverse side
also has a reverse side.

JAPANESE PROVERB

IF YOU WERE ME AND I WERE YOU

If you were me and I were you,
you'd have my eyes to see things through,
you'd feel my feelings like I do.
You'd always understand.

If you were me and I were you,
I'd walk for hours in your shoes,
I'd celebrate your point of view.
I'd always understand.

If you were me and I were you,
we'd question things we thought were true,
we'd try to change a mind or two.
We'd always understand.

REBECCA GARDYN LEVINGTON

DROPPING THE BALL

Did I hear that right?

                             I couldn't have.

Mum said it might happen one day –

                             I must have got it wrong.

I thought he was my friend.

                             I thought he was kind.

My face is hot.

                             Everyone's looking now.

But black people don't blush so

                             Maybe no one will notice.

I'll pretend I'm fine.

                             She's being so brave.

I know, I'll get the ball.

                             Should I say something?

I can't. I can't move.

                             Should I give her a hug?

(Did he even say it?)

                             I don't know.

"Stupid monkey."

                             I know, I'll get the ball.

My hands are shaking.

                             And hold her hand.

Oh! Maybe I'm not so

                             So she doesn't feel so

                alone.

ROCHELLE BURGESS & LAURA MUCHA

SPRING, 2020

Two months ago I wished for snow–
Miles and piles of wintry snow.
For whipping winds to blast and blow.
For school to close. For heaps of snow.

And now each day I yearn for school.
I miss my friends. My class was cool.
My brother pokes–says I'm a fool.
It snows in spring. I wish for school.

BUFFY SILVERMAN

QUESTIONS

Grown-ups are always asking,
When you grow up,
what do you want to be?

Like I need a label
stuck
to my identity.

How can I know
what
I want to be–

I'm still trying
to figure out
ME!

LINDA KULP TROUT

THE EARLIEST LIGHT

The earliest light
when the whole world's shapeshifting
and that includes me

LIZ GARTON SCANLON

ALL THINGS EXCEPT MYSELF I KNOW
excerpt

I KNOW when milk does flies contain;
   I know men by their bravery;
I know fair days from storm and rain;
   And what fruit apple-trees supply;
   And from their gums the trees descry;
I know when all things smoothly flow;
   I know who toil or idle lie;
All things except myself I know.

FRANÇOIS VILLON (1431–1463)

ALL THE WORLDS I LIVE IN

All the worlds I live in
All the worlds I see
Won't fit into one mouthful
When words spill out of me
Sometimes they're words of fire
That emerge with spark and flame
Sometimes they're gentle whispers
My worlds are not the same.

ALAN J. WRIGHT

When one door of happiness closes,
another opens; but often we look so long
at the closed door that we do not see the one
which has been opened for us.

HELEN KELLER

HELLO, FEAR

There I was, making tea in my kitchen,
when fear hit me like a school bus.
I didn't need a scientist or therapist
to tell me it hurt.
I screamed: *Arghh*! I shouted: *No!*

But after smashing into me,
fear just opened the folding glass door
of the bus, yanked me on,
then plopped me into a green vinyl seat.

I'm scared, I said.
Yeah, fear said. *'Cause I'm scary.*

Yeah, I squealed, as the bus careened
through the couch, through
my bedroom, through the splintering
dining room table.

What if I lose everything? I said to fear.
Yeah, said fear, *what if you do?*

And who will I be when everything changes?
Yeah, said fear, *who will you be?*

Then he opened the door
and shoved me off the bus
and I was standing again beside
the familiar green counter,
teacup in hand, not a drop spilled.

Who will you be? he shouted

from the half-open window.

I took a deep breath,
not knowing how to respond,
then stepped into my life,
determined to live into the answer.

ROSEMERRY WAHTOLA TROMMER

I AM BRAVE

Fear of monsters
Fear of dogs
Fear of hurricanes or bogs
Fear of spiders
Fear of feet
Fear of strangers in the street
Fear of anger
Fear of fear
Fear of losing someone dear
Fear of dragons
Fear of night
Fear of all the things that might
Or might not pass
Fear of being last in class

But fear's OK
Yes, fear's all right
For now I have it in my sight
And when I'm overwhelmed by fright
I recognize its painful bite
(And that is more than half the fight)

So yes I'm fearful, but I'm brave
And when my fear will not behave
I gently pat it on the head
And send it off to go to bed

LAURA MUCHA

INSTRUCTIONS FOR MY MIRROR

Love what you see
Be patient and kind
Keep expectations in check

Reflect my best self
Reject my objections
Cast no doubt or shadow

Focus my light
Frame my true beauty
Remind me that I am enough

MICHELLE HEIDENRICH BARNES

MY HOODY

I pledge allegiance to my hoody,
and the safety it
provides
me,
a life jacket in
troubled
seas,
and cover for me,
tender
teen.

LINDA MITCHELL

As far as the Moon is concerned,
he is always full.

TERRI GUILLEMETS

SEEING ME

They don't see me (not the *real* me)
crouching deep inside.
Not brave enough to stand up straight,
I'm not sure why I hide.

Could it be my shape and size?
(I feel like I'm too tall.)
I might trip over my own feet;
be laughed at when I fall.

Or maybe I'm nervous that
they'll see me, flaws and all,
and maybe they won't like it much.
I'll cringe at names they'd call...

    ...weird... nerdy... dumb... ?

I know there may be some of that.
I'll learn to let it go.
They might not know who they are yet,
but, as for me, I know:

    ...creative...caring... kind...

Being different means I'm me
and I don't need to fake!
The kids that don't get it (yet) –
well, it's just their mistake.

ALANA DEVITO

ROBERT SCHECHTER

UPSIDE-DOWN

Don't tell me that I'm upside-down!
My top's where it *should* be!
If you're convinced I'm flipped around,
then blame yourself, not me.

This kingdom isn't yours to rule.
You wear no monarch's crown.
Why can't you see I'm right-side-up?
It's *you* who's upside-down.

TO THE PANSY BY THE FRONT DOOR

I guess no one
told you
that you're an annual,
because every spring
your velvety-purple faces
tell me
"Spring is here."

Or maybe the other pansies did
tell you
"You're not winter hardy in this temperate zone."
But you just
ignore them,
hugging the foundation by the front door.
Hibernating
through the cold, dark Alaskan winter,
until the last muddy remnants
of winter's snow
have melted.

Then,
you emerge.

Your velvety-purple faces
tell me
that I don't have to listen
to what other people
tell me.

ELISABETH NORTON

BACKYARD DANDELIONS

(1)

Mom weaving yellow
flowers into a golden
crown for my sister.

(2)

Missy skipping round
and round, blowing wishes on
white, cottony puffs.

(3)

Goldfinches pecking
at seed heads, seeking the sweet
prizes left behind.

(4)

Dad pointing at the
"weeds," saying he'll pay well if
I pull them all up.

(5)

Me, smiling at how
dandelions scored me a
new videogame.

CARMELA A. MARTINO

Writing can be your magic carpet ride through
just about anything.

SAGE COHEN

WHEN I WRITE

When I write,
most often
I'm not writing stories.
Instead, I'm trying
to make sense
of my own story—
sifting through my history,
creating my identity,
building myself,
one
word
at
a
time.

MOLLY HOGAN

FINGERPRINT
an In One Word poem

There's a tiger in my fingerprint.
And fret and tire and ping.
And maybe also ripening:
ignite and fire and ring.

On grey days there's no tiger,
just pine, inept, infringe.
I cannot roar with pen or print
there's only grief and only rip

But maybe also...
tiger grit.

APRIL HALPRIN WAYLAND

YOUR GUESS

If you really knew me,
If you could see right through me,
If you could glimpse the true me,
If you could rightly view me,
I wonder if you'd like me more, or less?

I wonder if you'd flee me,
If you could clearly see me,
Know what it's like to be me,
Without the need to dream me,
And if I'm really like the way you guess?

ROBERT SCHECHTER

EMBRACE MISTAKES

When you hit a snag
and stumble,
do you feel a grumble rumble?
When your best plans turn
to rubble,
does your anger start to bubble?
Does it boil toward a fit?
Do you want to shout:
"I QUIT!"
If a setback's plaguing you,
take a *b r e a t h*
and try this view:
    Don't get irate,
    recalculate.
    Don't make a fuss,
    rethink, discuss.
If you persist and don't give up,
at some point you'll break through.
A problem's not a roadblock.
It's your path to something new!

MICHELLE SCHAUB

It takes a lot of courage and strength
to change yourself. You need to be brave
enough to look at what is better for you
and change for that.

MATT HAIG

ABSOLUTES

I found a pair of magic glasses, so I tried them on.
They changed the way I saw my life–all in-betweens were gone!

I suddenly became convinced my options were extreme:
I'd either burst with confidence or have no self-esteem.

I'd either be hilarious or tediously dull.
I'd either be a genius or have nothing in my skull.

I'd either always win or be a loser through and through.
I'd either know my future or proceed without a clue.

But thankfully, I took those glasses off before too long,
since all those absolutes I saw were *absolutely* wrong!

LISA VARCHOL PERRON

WHEN I CRY

There is a monster in me
called Sadness. Its arms and legs
ache. It is weary, as if
it spent all night walking
across steep mountains.

There is a monster in me
whose hair stretches from its head
in tangled rivers,
flowing fast as the thoughts
that won't let me sleep.

When I cry, Monster weeps.
Tears crawl on eight fuzzy legs
like spiders down its cheeks.
They tickle! Monster laughs so hard
its teeth turn pink.

Can I laugh too, even though
I am sad? *"Yes,"* Monster says.
You're a weary, silly, laughing,
weeping, wonderful creature.

LAURA SHOVAN

SENSIBILITY

Thy heart so sweetly sensitive,
    Is like an April sky;
      One moment sunshine, and the next
      Dark shadows o'er it fly.

One little ray lights up thy soul
    To gladness, joy and mirth;
      One little cloud o'ershades the whole,
      And bows it down to earth.

SIMEON CARTER

WHAT CONFIDENCE KNOWS ABOUT ME

That my belief in myself is brief.
The slightest upset can
shatter it,
scatter it,
like a sheaf of papers in the wind.

That my assurance has no endurance.
That doubt is always waiting
to unsettle me,
like a thief,
ready to rob me of my mettle.

That an approving nod, a job well done,
Can renew my fortitude,
adjust my attitude
and, like sunlight on a leaf,

give me strength to grow on.

CATHERINE FLYNN

WINDOW

Night from a railroad car window
Is a great, dark soft thing
Broken across with slashes of light.

CARL SANDBURG

REFLECTION
a golden shovel

Bent but not **broken**
I stare **across**
my stormy life, **with**
thunderous mistakes, few **slashes**
of wisdom, yet a glimmer **of**
rainbow **light.**

MICHELLE HEIDENRICH BARNES

A little more persistence, a little more effort,
and what seemed hopeless failure
may turn to glorious success.

ELBERT HUBBARD

GROWING PERSPECTIVE

I seemed to be buried
beneath my mistake.
The pressure kept mounting.
I felt I would break.

But that's when I saw it,
a tiny, stray seed.
I planted it firmly
for it to be freed.

With time and persistence,
it broke through the ground
and blossomed with beauty.
The truth was profound.

While stressed by my error,
I'd failed to foresee
I needed to grow
into who I would be.

Not buried, but planted.
A new point of view.
I'm stronger than ever.
Through hardship, I grew.

TRICIA TORRIBLE

STACKING GRAMPA'S FIREWOOD

I agreed to help Grampa stack up his new wood,
but perhaps, on reflection, I misunderstood.

I really don't think we can move this whole pile.
It's a mountain of logs! It goes up for a mile!

I have landed myself in a terrible fix.
It will take us a year to stack up all these sticks!

But wait–Grampa's started. He's already made
a column of logs, straight and true, neatly laid.

I pull on my gloves, throw some logs in the cart,
wheel it over to Grampa–at least that's a start.

Then I pick up a log, and I add to his row.
Stick by stick, one by one, our new stack starts to grow.

I move log after log, adding one at a time,
until slowly but surely, our pile starts to climb.

As I carry and lug, my old outlook has changed.
We are moving the mountain! Our wood's re-arranged.

Our tall, squared-up stack is a sight to behold,
and Grampa's all set for the long winter's cold.

CHRISTY MIHALY

SOMETHING BEATS OUT NOTHING

What's the point in trying
when I can't do it all?
Something beats out nothing.
So I'll do something small.

It may not be perfect.
I'll do it anyway.
Something beats out nothing.
I'll do one thing today.

ABBY N. WOOLDRIDGE

STRIVING

An 88
On a test

Is that close to
Excellent
Or far from
Perfect?

A 2nd place
Finish

Is that an
Almost-win
Or just
Another loss?

You gain
Something
Trying hard
Even if
The medal isn't gold
The score isn't perfect
The race isn't won

Getting in the game
Giving it your all
Isn't that everything?

SYDNEY DUNLAP

THE ATTEMPT

a poem in two voices

I can't do it.
This is stupid.

        I will figure out
        a way.

I'm not smart.
I'll never get it.

        I will practice
        every day.

What's the point
of even trying,
when I know
I'll only fail?

        If I try,
        and keep on trying,
        I <u>will</u> get it.
        I won't bail.

This is really,
<u>really</u> hard.

        This is really,
        <u>really</u> hard.

Oh, forget it!

        I can't get it,

I can't get it.

        yet.

REBECCA GARDYN LEVINGTON

PERSEVERE

I watched a spider work its weave –
It stayed on task, no sigh nor heave.
It took awhile but it did achieve
excellence hard not to perceive.

I watched the waves ebb and flow
they washed a pebble to and fro
until they reached it to my toe –
how long it took, I do not know.

But s l o w l y it dawned on me –
I cannot let things just come to me.
If I'm at it diligently,
things'll work out, they'll come to be!

MARZIEH ABBAS

OPENING THE DOOR

Down the narrow hall,
a dark and shadowed way,
you walk what seems entirely
a path too far away.

Where's the switch to draw the light?
Perhaps there is just none.
Adjust your eyes and don't look back –
this may not be such fun.

Shuffle on and watch your step,
mind stumbling blocks that try!
Keep steady footsteps to the door,
no time to moan or cry.

Miles before you stretch each day
before it comes in view;
behind you one door has been closed –
it's not the door for you.

Step over hurdles, look around,
and keep your focus keen;
for as you near that door you'll know
new treasures yet unseen.

Look, the door is straight ahead,
and fingertips can reach.
Stop a moment and look back
what lessons did life teach?

Put hand to doorknob, give a twist,
and then a gentle pull;

Ah, my friend, behind that door
The meaning will be full.

Standing there quite breathless
without regret or doubt,
your path has led you to the place
this journey was about.

DONNA JT SMITH

KEEP A-PLUGGIN' AWAY
excerpt

Delve away beneath the surface,
There is treasure farther down,--
Keep a-pluggin' away.

Let the rain come down in torrents,
Let the threat'ning heavens frown,
Keep a-pluggin' away.

When the clouds have rolled away,
There will come a brighter day
All your labor to repay,--
Keep a-pluggin' away.

PAUL LAURENCE DUNBAR

A day of worry is more exhausting
than a week of work.

JOHN LUBBOCK

SLEEPLESS

Could I be the only one

still awake this late in bed,

movies looping through my head

of all the things I should have said,

of all the things I should have done?

Could I be the only one?

SUZY LEVINSON

RUMINATION

It's over,
so why
does my brain want to
revisit
reimagine
recreate
What I COULD have said
What I SHOULD have said?

As hard as I try
to get it right
in all these scenarios,
I will
never change what has already happened.

Perhaps I should
stop the endless imagining
of what might have been
give myself a break
and know that I have surely learned
surely grown
and will surely
do better
next time.

SYDNEY DUNLAP

WEIGHTLESS

At times when I feel weighted down by things that seem unfair,
I dream of life in outer space, of floating light as air.
I wake up oh-so-weightless, fly with friends to school at eight.
I hover during homeroom, soar in art as I create.

I chase my lunch as it strays off and catch a bite mid-flight.
I coast in chem and sail though essays when it's time to write.
Then heading home, I freewheel on my astronautic bike.
My Saint Bernard becomes a kite out on our stellar hike.

At night as I spin off to sleep, I find my mind is clear.
My heavy thoughts have drifted off into the atmosphere.
Without the pull of gravity, I float through cosmic hush,
past constellations, shooting stars, and sparkling, astral dust.

I bring the feeling of free-floating back to Earth with me.
I'm ready to let worries go—I'm weightless and carefree.

HELEN KEMP ZAX

THE ROAD TO BECOMING

What would
you have done
if you knew
where this path
led to? Would
you have taken
another, dis-
regarding the
good things
that happened
along the way?
  You can't go
    back, but you
       can still turn
         the corner. You
           alone can change
             your mind.

MICHELLE HEIDENRICH BARNES

TRANSFORMATION

I was a Sick Girl
five years of my 8-year-old life, long enough
to grow accustomed to the role of Sick Girl.

Playing across the street with my friend,
Margaret, it was my first solo play time
after a life-saving operation put an end

to certain death. Margaret and I were swinging
when an old woman in a hat asked across the fence,
How's the little sick girl doing?

I, Sick Girl, assumed she meant me:
I'm better, thank you. But, surprise,
she didn't mean me.

No, not you, Old Woman replied. *Margaret
has been sick.* Old Woman jolted me onto
my journey toward health that I took with no regret.

So I was not the sole Sick Girl on our street,
nor in Detroit, Michigan, nor the USA, nor the world—
Old Woman, you changed my perspective, quite a feat.

I changed my life because of your remark—
though I cannot form a memory picture of you now—
and unfeeling as your remark was, stark.

KATHLEEN MCKINLEY HARRIS

THE LAND OF BLUE

Across the valley it waits for you,
a place they call The Land of Blue.

It's far and near, it's strange yet known –
and in this land you'll feel alone,
you might feel tears roll down your cheek,
you might feel wobbly, weary, weak.

I know this won't sound fun to you –
it's not – this is The Land of Blue.
It's blue – not gold or tangerine,
it's dark – not light, not bright or clean.

It's blue – and when you leave, you'll see
the crackly branches of the tree,
the golden skies, the purring cat,
the piercing eyes, the feathered hat

and all the other things that come
when you escape from feeling glum.

Across the valley it waits for you,
a place they call The Land of Blue
and going there will help you know
how others feel when they feel low.

LAURA MUCHA

WHAT YOU DON'T SEE

How easy it is for me
to get lost in my head.

How following directions in class
is doubly hard
when you interrupt
to add extra details or
a story or tell that kid
to sit down again.

How doing anything
while you watch me
is impossible
as I wonder what
mistakes you see
and then, I freeze.
Unable to continue.

I wish you knew
how to help me
succeed with ADHD.

LINDA MITCHELL

GRAY MATTER

The Brain–
    folds like an origami elephant
    flap over flap
    no crease makes sense
    until you see the elephant.

MARGARET SIMON

YOU NEVER CAN TELL

excerpt

You never can tell what your thoughts will do,
 In bringing you hate or love;
For thoughts are things, and their airy wings
 Are swifter than carrier doves.
They follow the law of the universe--
 Each thing must create its kind,
And they speed o'er the track to bring you back
 Whatever went out from your mind.

ELLA WHEELER WILCOX

The world always seems brighter
when you've just made something
that wasn't there before.

NEIL GAIMAN

I WAS SAD

Last night I was sad
so I wrote a poem.

This morning I am still sad
but there's a poem
that didn't exist
this time yesterday.

RUTH HERSEY

LINES OF PERSPECTIVE

What is the difference between "draw" and "sketch"?
She's trying to teach us; so far it's a stretch.

Drawings take time, she says: keen observation.
Sketches are quick, she says: broad illustration.

Drawings require you to inhale the detail;
Sketches are more of a large-scale exhale.

You grab it, you get it, a few marks and lines
Is all that you need for a sketch to remind

You of what you have wondered, imagined or seen.
Drawing's voluptuous; sketches are lean.

Drawing is drawn-out, examined, revised---
Sketch scratches an itch that you feel in your eyes.

HEIDI MORDHORST

THE ART TEACHER SAID

She said to draw an animal. *Pick any one and go for it!*
I don't draw animals. I used to try. They never looked right.
Now I don't try.

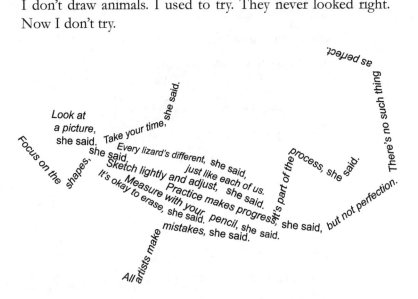

She said and she said and she said and she said...
and she kept coming back to see the nothing I had done.

So I guess I have to try.   And try.   And try.

. . . .

It's not perfect, but it's not too bad... it may be my best one
yet...

I   think   I'll   give   it

another

try.

ALANA DEVITO

STONES AND FEATHERS

Some words, like stones, are heavy–
they knock me to my knees.
While others float like feathers
and scatter in the breeze.

The weighty words are insults
repeating in my mind.
The words I let escape me
are generous and kind.

But I can start refusing
to carry stony things.
I'll gather all my feathers
and stitch them into WINGS.

LISA VARCHOL PERRON

A COLORFUL THOUGHT:

blue is a devoted
handmaiden to sadness

give her a summer sky
a blooming hydrangea and
she may look for a new job

DIANE MAYR

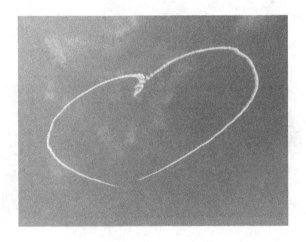

SINCE MY HOUSE BURNED DOWN
haiku

Since my house burned down
I now own a better view
of the rising moon

MIZUTA MASAHIDE

Slow breathing is like an anchor
in the midst of an emotional storm:
the anchor won't make the storm go away,
but it will hold you steady until it passes.

RUSS HARRIS

NIGHT JOURNEY

Breathe with me–

Bring nighttime's

breath

untethered

relaxed

sleeping through

legs light

calm body

breathe s-l-o-w-l-y

deep, full, breaths

without effort…

Bring me

refreshed to

morning's rise

ready to carry

rhythm

into day

with

confidence

and

challenge

and

invitation

for

what

comes

next

MICHELLE KOGAN

BE STILL IN THE WORLD

Be still in the world wherever you are,
listen to life's lullaby,
the heartbeat, the breathing, the giving, receiving,
the sun and the moon and the star.

They all shine true through the essence of you,
a beacon of boundless light,
the father, the mother, the sister, the brother,
all are within you tonight.

Let the flow of the seas, the lilt of the breeze,
the rush and the calm of all time
carry your dreams along rivers and streams
and let you be still where you are.

CHARLES GHIGNA

THIS MORNING

Begin this day, mindful of the world and those I love,
mindful of my ancestors' blessings

Begin this day, believing in my creative self
Begin this day by opening my mind, my heart

Begin this day by focusing on the sights, the sounds
of my surroundings, the secrets of the natural world

Begin this day with the hope for possibilities to arrive
Begin this day, seeking the wonders, the curiosities of the earth

Begin this day imagining and seeing things
from a kaleidoscope perspective

Begin this day full of joy
Begin this day ready to flourish where I am

JONE RUSH MACCULLOCH

I DON'T KNOW

Today, I notice something green
spearing through the dirt
in the garden, and only
because there are eight such spears
rising in perfect rows do I vaguely remember
last year I planted bulbs there,
but I don't remember what they are.
How much of the beauty we plant
do we forget?

There is so much in me that grows
because of words you have sown.
I doubt you remember them,
I don't remember them, either,
only that your words were kind
and now they have taken root.

Who knows what the flowers
will look like? I water them, though,
trust I'll be delighted when they bloom
into a garden of beautiful I don't know.

ROSEMERRY WAHTOLA TROMMER

SATISFIED

My life is very boring
and I'm thankful it is so.
I'm not a fan of soaring.
I prefer to stay down low.

The sky can make me dizzy
just by being overhead.
I'm healthy and I'm happy.
I sleep soundly in my bed.

It's quite enough excitement
just to be alive, I say.
Who needs complications?
Nothing beats a boring day.

ROBERT SCHECHTER

SMART COOKIE
after Wallace Stevens

The fortune that you seek is in another cookie,
was my fortune. So I'll be equally frank– the wisdom
that you covet is in another poem. The life that you desire
is in a different universe. The cookie you are craving
is in another jar. The jar is buried somewhere in Tennessee.
Don't even think of searching for it. If you found that jar,
everything would go kerflooey for a thousand miles around.
It is the jar of your fate in an alternate reality. Don't even
think of living that life. Don't even think of eating that
cookie. Be a smart cookie– eat what's on your plate, not in
some jar in Tennessee. That's my wisdom for today, though I
know it's not what you were looking for.

RICHARD SCHIFFMAN

WHAT YOU WANT

When what you want
is to swim laps in a pool,
a walk in the neighborhood
will have to do.

When what you want
is a hug and high five,
a card or an email
will have to suffice.

When what you want
leaves you high and dry
what you DO have
will just have to satisfy.

MARY LEE HAHN

Three grand essentials to happiness
in this life are something to do,
something to love,
and something to hope for.

JOSEPH ADDISON

EACH NEW DAY RISES

Each new day rises
whole and warm and promising
so don't you give up

LIZ GARTON SCANLON

HOPE

Hope has a
lollipop middle–
a floaty, sticky
swirl of color,
spiral-light.

Have a
little lick
and it
will lift
you
upright.

TABATHA YEATTS

THE SHADOW OF A BUTTERFLY

looks exactly as one would expect,
a darkness marking the presence of beauty
yet unseen but still within reach

for those who, with but a tilt of their head,
come to see themselves in a creature whose resplendence
is not made any less striking by the shadow self
forever fading in and out of sight

ROBYN FOHOUO

THOUGHTS

Thoughts do not need the wings of words
    To fly to any goal.
Like subtle lightnings, not like birds,
    They speed from soul to soul.

Hide in your heart a bitter thought
    Still it has power to blight.
Think Love, although you speak it not,
    It gives the world more light.

ELLA WHEELER WILCOX

THE SEARCH FOR BETTER DAYS

I hold no wish
For a heavy heart.
I must nourish my thoughts
with hope and humour.
I must feed them with a belief
That we will emerge wiser,
Stronger
From these days.

ALAN J. WRIGHT

SIDEWALK GREETING

Chalk art on sidewalks
greet passersby with colors
"This too shall pass!"

MARGARET SIMON

HOPE AND FAITH

excerpt

HOPE! Not distant is the Springtime,
   Butterflies will soon be winging–
In new nests the merry songsters
   Their new songs will soon be singing.

Know! The night itself will vanish,
   Cloudlands drift and melt away–
Once again will skies shine azure,
   Stars by night and suns by day.

ISAAC LEIB PEREZ
(translated by Henry Goodman)

FALL IN LOVE
WITH THE YOU OF RIGHT NOW

regardless

of how

right now

is going.

APRIL HALPRIN WAYLAND

A found poem from text by Lori Snyder

RAINBOW
an ekphrastic acrostic

Rain pauses.
Arise, heart! Feed yourself with colored light.
Indulge! Feast your eyes. Summon your songs.
Now, find those oars,
Bend your back to head for shore.
Outlaster of storms, open
Wide and sing.

TABATHA YEATTS

You can't go back and make a new start,
but you can start right now
and make a brand new ending.

JAMES R. SHERMAN

SUPPORTING HEALTHY THINKING

How do you talk to yourself? Are you fair and supportive, rooting for yourself to succeed? Maybe sometimes you are your own biggest critic.

Let's say you forgot to study for a test (you forgot to write down what day it would be) and you did badly. It makes total sense to be annoyed that Past-You put Present-You in a tough situation. But you have to ask yourself...What would help Future-You the most?

Being mad at yourself can motivate you, or it can immobilize you. Sometimes people feel so badly about their own behavior that they don't try to change. Sometimes people start out with a reasonable complaint about their own behavior but then it spirals out of proportion.

In the case above, thinking "Next time I want to be sure to remember, so what can I do to make that happen?" is more helpful than thinking, "Wow, I am such a mess that I am bound to fail."

If you are used to talking to yourself negatively, it can be hard to shift to a more encouraging voice, but it is possible (and SO worth it!). Try to notice when you are giving yourself a hard time and replace negative statements with positive (or neutral) ones. You can even write them down to help yourself make substitutions. You are making a new habit, so it's not going to happen all at once. Give yourself time.

If you have any "friends" who talk negatively to you, they may be contributing to your negative self-talk. You deserve better! Family members can also be overly critical. Having a compassionate inner voice for yourself is essential.

It's important that when you talk to yourself, you acknowledge your mistakes, but you also encourage yourself about the future. You CAN do things differently. Remind yourself that!

Remember what businessperson and therapist Wendy Morgan would say when asked how she was doing: "I've got good potential!"

CALMING YOURSELF DOWN

Some people like to walk outside or go for a run when they are feeling tense. Those are great things to do! If you need to relax and you can't go outside, you still have options.

When I am feeling stressed, the back of my neck feels tight. If I am especially anxious, my stomach feels as though it is full of butterflies. Our bodies respond to our emotions. It can go both ways – if we can calm our bodies down, we can calm down our emotions.

One thing I like to do when my neck is stiff is lift my shoulders as high as I can toward my ears, hold this position for ten seconds, and then relax. Tensing and relaxing your muscles is something you can do to feel better quickly. You can start with curling your toes for ten seconds and move upward: lift your feet, tense your legs, tighten your abdomen, make a fist, raise your shoulders. But if you want to just pick the tensest parts of your body to focus on, that works too.

Another way to release tension is to take deep breaths. Here are some possible techniques you can experiment with:

Wave breathing
As you breathe in, imagine a wave rolling in. Breathe out imagining the wave rolling out. You can imagine the sounds of the waves as you go.

Color breathing
Breathe in imagining the air is a color. Breathe out a different color. When I do this one, I imagine different colors every time. Picture whatever colors you like.

Hand breathing

Spread out the fingers of one hand and trace the fingers with the other hand as you breathe – up as you take a breath in, and down as you breathe out.

One last thing – don't forget that writing can help! Writing down your worries can help you think through a solution. Writing poems or songs can also make you feel better.

POEM FORMS YOU CAN TRY

ACROSTIC
In an acrostic poem, the first letter of each line spells out a word. Sometimes people will have the first word of each line create a message. **Rainbow** by Tabatha Yeatts spells "rainbow" when the first letters are read vertically. **Rainbow** is an ekphrastic acrostic (read about ekphrastic poems below).

CONCRETE POEM
A concrete poem (also called a shape poem) is one where the shape of the poem matches the topic. For instance, you could write one in the shape of a teardrop about crying, a bat about baseball, or a sun about summer. You can make a concrete poem where the words draw something complicated, like the lizard in **The Art Teacher Said** by Alana DeVito. Another option is making something subtle, like **The Road to Becoming** by Michelle Heidenrich Barnes.

EKPHRASTIC
An ekphrastic poem is a poem written about a work of art. It could be a painting, like the one in **Rainbow** by Tabatha Yeatts, or it could be any kind of art. Usually ekphrastic poems are inspired by visual art, but you could even use a dance performance or music. The key is that your poem is "in conversation" with another work of art.

GOLDEN SHOVEL
Terrance Hayes invented Golden Shovel poems. To write a Golden Shovel, take a line (or more) of another poem and have it be the last word of each line of your poem. Golden Shovels are a bit similar to acrostics, except your chosen words go at the end of the line instead of at the beginning. **Reflection** by Michelle Heidenrich Barnes is a Golden Shovel

poem which uses a line from **Window** by Carl Sandburg.

IN ONE WORD POEM

April Halprin Wayland invented In One Word poems. Choose a word and then write a poem that includes words formed from letters of your original word. In the poem **Fingerprint**, April includes 16 words made out of the letters of "fingerprint." You can look on Wordmaker.info to see the words within your One Word or you can find the words yourself. The word "perspective" has 99 five-letter words and 81 four-letter words to choose from!

ACKNOWLEDGMENTS

A Warm Morning appears courtesy photographer Marco Nürnberger, Creative Commons licensing.

Be Still in the World by Charles Ghigna appeared in *Illusions: Poetry & Art for the Young at Heart*, Resource Publications, 2020.

Church Door appears courtesy photographer Rodney Campbell, Creative Commons licensing.

Cute french bulldog portrait appears courtesy Nenad Stojkovic, Creative Commons licensing.

Dropping the Ball by Rochelle Burgess and Laura Mucha appeared in *Being Me*, Otter-Barry Books, 2021.

Feather appears courtesy photographer flattop341, Creative Commons licensing.

Fingerprint appears courtesy TNS Sofres, Creative Commons licensing.

Full Moon over Margarita appears courtesy photographer Bill Mulder, Creative Commons licensing.

Happy birthday to me appears courtesy Emran Kassim, Creative Commons licensing.

I Am Brave by Laura Mucha appeared in *Dear Ugly Sisters*, Otter-Barry Books, 2020.

It's been a long time appears courtesy kcxd, Creative Commons licensing.

Lotus and Bud appears courtesy photographer Liz West, Creative Commons licensing.

Morning Light Rays appears courtesy photographer Raita Futo, Creative Commons licensing.

Origami elephants appears courtesy of Jnzl's Photos, Creative Commons licensing.

Rainbow is by Nikolay Dubovskoy and is in the public domain.

School Bus Door appears courtesy photographer stockicide, Creative Commons licensing.

Sensibility by Simeon Carter appeared in *Poems and Aphorisms: A Woodman's Musings*, 1893, and is in the public domain.

Smart Cookie by Richard Schiffman appeared in *What the Dust Doesn't Know*, Salmon Poetry.

The Land of Blue by Laura Mucha appeared in *A Poem For Every Day of the Year,* Macmillan, 2017.

This too shall pass appears courtesy Margaret Simon.

Thought Machine by Laura Mucha appeared in *Being Me,* Otter-Barry Books, 2021.

Try Baby Steps appears courtesy photographer Brett Jordan, Creative Commons licensing.

CPSIA information can be obtained
at www.ICGtesting.com
Printed in the USA
LVHW081823010422
714996LV00001B/45